THERE are many aspects of Scotland and Scottish life which are known throughout the world. The more traditional trappings of tartan, bagpipes, haggis and shortbread are instantly recognised everywhere as almost a national trademark. The poems of the 'ploughman poet', Robert Burns, are admired internationally, January the 25th sees Burns' Night celebrations around the globe, while other literary figures, like Sir Walter Scott and Robert Louis Stevenson, have their works translated into many languages.

Scotland is also known as the birthplace of golf, in honour of the game's beginnings at St Andrews and also of television, invented by John Logie Baird. 'Scotch' whisky is a well loved export and, while Scotland's history has become the subject of major Hollywood movies, the nation itself draws tourists from every corner of the world.

Another thing for which Scots can feel justifiably proud is their sense of humour. Whether it's laughing in the face of adversity or finding humour in the absurdities of life, the Scots know you can't beat a good laugh.

Collected in this volume are classic comic strips from the pages of The Sunday Post Fun Section. Aiming to brighten up even the dullest of Sunday mornings, The Fun Section has kept Scots laughing for over six decades. At home or abroad, Oor Wullie and The Broons have built up a vast and loyal following among readers who can't resist the characters' antics.

The Broons and Oor Wullie occupy a special place, both in the hearts and near the funny bones of their fans. The fans themselves come from all walks of life and, as you will see, count some familiar faces among their numbers. Some of these famous folk will be telling us why these funny folk are so special to them.

Join us now for a sightseeing tour, looking at life in Scotland through the eyes of the residents of Number 10 Glebe Street and a cheeky wee scamp.

THE BROONS AND OOR WULLIE — A NATION'S FAVOURITES!

5

SPORT

Sir Alex Ferguson CBE is made a Freeman of the City of Aberdeen!

Alex Ferguson CBE

The Den of football management

Paw checks the football scores.

ONE thing the Scots, as a nation, are passionate about is sport. From the World Cup to a kick-about in the park, Scotland is a nation of sportsmen and women. And it doesn't stop at football, even if that is sometimes described as 'our national game'. Scotland has produced world class performers at rugby, golf, boxing and snooker, with an army of admirers watching from the crowd, or from the comfort of their own sofas. And there is no shortage of up and coming hopefuls, waiting to carry on the tradition.

One man who has achieved European success on both sides of the Border is Sir Alex Ferguson CBE, as manager of both Aberdeen and Manchester United Football Clubs. While these are memorable victories, Sir Alex, referring to the Broons and Oor Wullie, says he has "plenty of memories". His favourite character is Paw and he says, "All kids in Scotland read the Broons."

Another big name from the world of football is Ally McCoist. Aside from making his name in the field as a striker for Rangers, he also now fields tricky questions on BBC's "A Question Of Sport", whilst asking the

Ally McCoist, waiting to answer "A Question Of Sport".

knew the Broons, but I was an avid fan of Oor Wullie."

How about a favourite Oor Wullie strip? "I fear I loved them all; no particular favourite after all these years." Rob also added, "My big moment was when I had the honour of sitting next to the wee man and his bucket in a photoshoot."

As proud sports supporters and, sometimes, players, The Broons and Wullie would be delighted with the support from these famous fans. Turn the page now to witness some of the Fun Section's sporting classics . . . and catastrophes.

Rob Wainwright in action for Scotland.

Athletic Hen? In your dreams.

JINGS! WHIT A BRAW THING TO SAY!

...uestions himself as co-host of "McCoist And ...cCauley". When asked for a favourite ...roons character, Ally came up with Hen as ...ead and shoulders ahead of the rest and ...ays his most vivid Broons memory is "getting ...y Broons Book fae Santa."

...oving on from football, Rob Wainwright, ...rmer captain of the Scotland Rugby Team, ...ow a regular newspaper columnist, was ...appy to tackle a few questions we pitched ...m. When asked to name his favourite ...roons character, Rob replied, "Sadly, I never

The Sunday Post 24th February 1946

The Sunday Post 10th September 1950

SPORT

The Sunday Post 13th August 1950

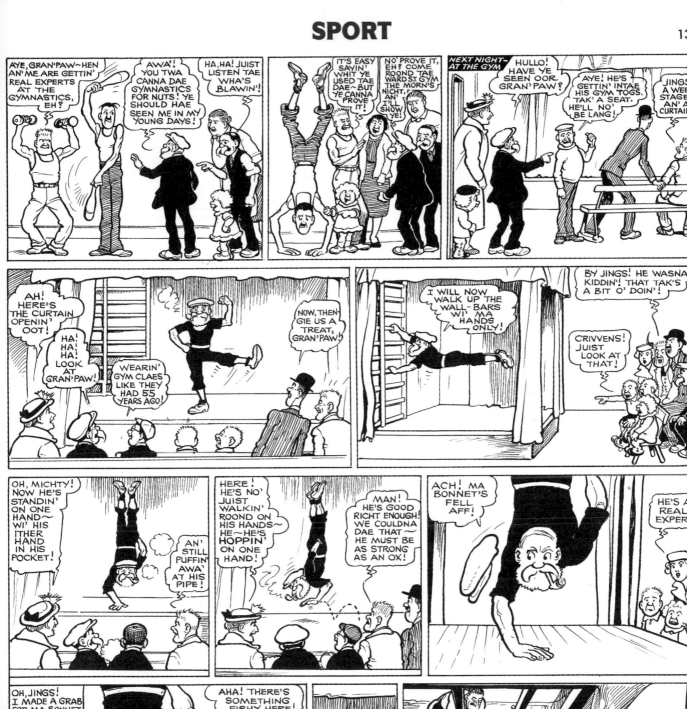

The Sunday Post 29th April 1951
For several weeks in 1951, the Broons were 'at war' with their
neighbours, the Blacks. The story printed above shows the conclusion to the feud.

The Sunday Post 1st December 1957

The Sunday Post 23rd August 1953

The Sunday Post 26th June 1966

The Sunday Post 23rd August 1964

HOLIDAYS

DOROTHY PAUL is an actress and comedienne, known for her appearances in plays, such as the smash-hit, "The Steamie", as well as her one-woman shows. She is also a Broons fan, saying, "I like them all, but Daphne would be my favourite. She's very plain." Plain speaking there.

Asked for her most vivid recollection of the famous family, Dorothy says, "I always enjoyed stories when the family were at the But 'n' Ben for holidays." And, while she says, "Not one in particular," when asked to select a favourite story, she adds, "We all grew up with the Broons and Oor Wullie. They're part of Scottish Heritage and they should never be stopped."

Best selling author, Rosamunde Pilcher is well known for her works of romantic fiction, but still finds time for a chuckle with the Broons. "I never met the Broons until after the War, when I was married," she says, "but my children and grandchildren all read them avidly." Her favourite in the family is Maw, and she, like Dorothy, has fond memories of, "The Broons going off on holiday to their But 'n' Ben in the country."

Be it But 'n' Ben or a Barbados beach, everyone needs a holiday now and again. Even comic characters, as we'll see, over the following pages.

Dorothy Paul enterta

Daphne is 'plainly' dismayed.

The first visit to the But 'n' Ben was on the 26th May, 1940.

Holidays in Scotland in times past. Outdoor swimming pools which would daunt a polar bear. Lightning fast putting greens and crazy golf. The silver sands of Morar. Fish suppers on The East Neuk of Fife. Day trips to Edinburgh Castle, and the one o'clock gun. Rothesay, immortalised in song, Largs and Dunoon. The Trossachs and Loch Lomond. Aberdeen and the North East coast towns. The road to the Isles.

Paw Broon, always the shipyard worker, who preferred boats to planes. His logic was simple. If something went wrong with the boat, he could swim a wee bit. And just how often did those "Fair" fortnights live up to their name?

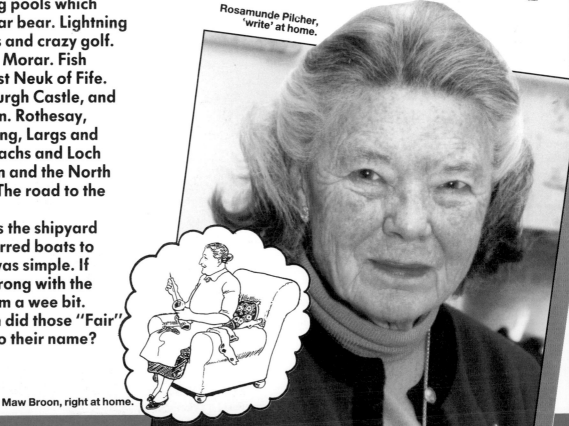

Rosamunde Pilcher, 'write' at home.

Maw Broon, right at home.

HOLIDAYS

The Sunday Post 1st December 1946

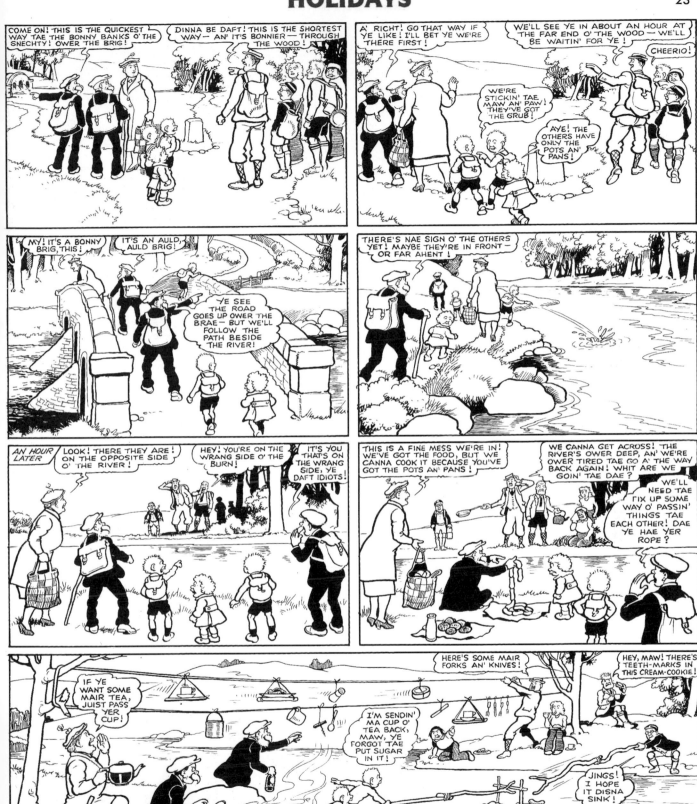

The Sunday Post 9th June 1946

HOLIDAYS

The Sunday Post 17th July 1949

The Sunday Post 10th August 1952

HOLIDAYS

The Sunday Post 11th August 1963

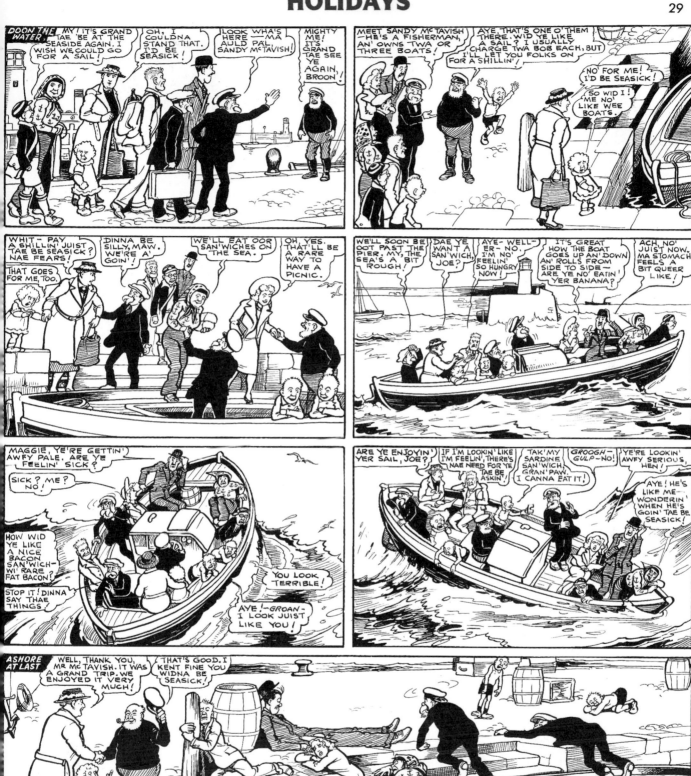

HOLIDAYS

HOLIDAYS

31

The Sunday Post 10th May 1953

HOLIDAYS

The Sunday Post 14th March 1954

SPECIAL DAYS

LIKE most people, THE BROONS AND OOR WULLIE have days they really look forward to, from Easter, with the traditional rolling of eggs, to Christmas, when the bairns can't wait for Santa to bring them presents.

In this section, we share some special occasions with the Fun Section folk, so here's a chance to go "guising" at Hallowe'en, neep lantern in hand, first footing after the bells and playing tricks on April Fool's Day, without having to wait for the months to roll by.

SPECIAL DAYS

The Sunday Post 25th December 1949

The Sunday Post 13th April 1952

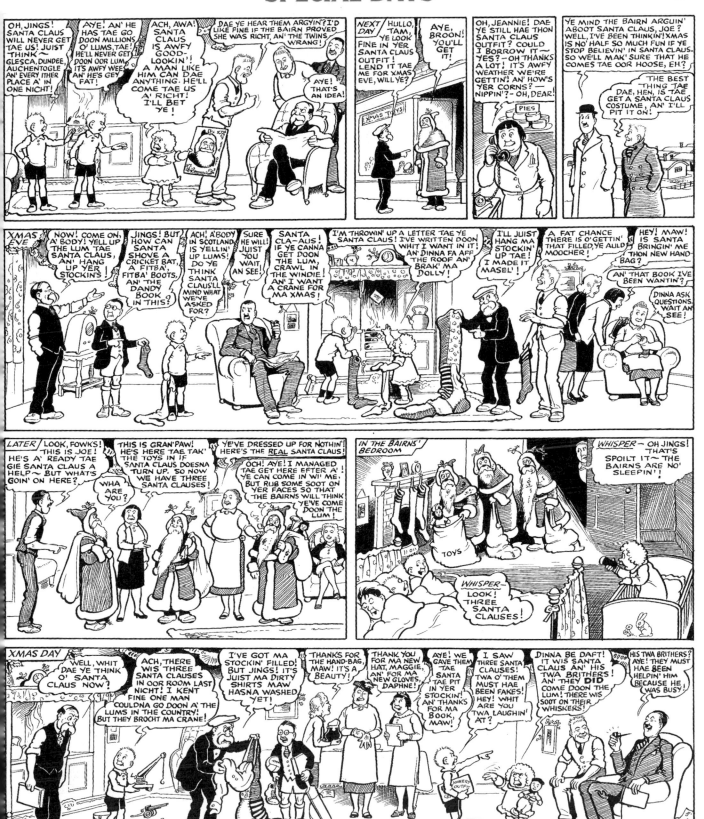

The Sunday Post 25th October 1964

The Sunday Post 21st December 1947

The Sunday Post 24th December 1967

The Sunday Post 28th December 1947

The Sunday Post 31st March 1968

The Sunday Post 2nd January 1949

The Sunday Post 29th December 1968

The Sunday Post 26th December 1954

ENTERTAINME

THE BROONS AND OOR WULLIE have kept the nation entertained for sixty years, but how do they entertain themselves? In the following pages, we see them at the pictures, visiting the circus and funfair and watching telly.

A familiar face from telly is actress Gwyneth Guthrie, one of the stars of Scotland's very own soap opera. 'High Road' has recently celebrated its twentieth anniversary on our TV screens and, as busybody Mrs Mack, Gwyneth has become one of its best loved characters.

One of Gwyneth's own best loved characters is Granpaw Broon. She says, "He's such a funny old man and I love the way he's drawn." She doesn't have a favourite strip, saying "I love all the characters and have become very attached to them," adding a vivid memory of The Broons. "I wouldn't read any of the news pages of the paper. I was always interested in getting out The Broons section. I would take it to a quiet place and read it back to front."

Another of Gwyneth's Broons memories involves another well loved Scottish actor, Iain Cuthbertson, probably best known for his role as Charles Endell, Esquire, in "Budgie". "I went to visit Iain Cuthbertson when he took ill and asked him what he would like me to bring. His response was, the one thing that would cheer him up was the 'Broons Annual', and that's what I took him." She also adds, "I still buy the annuals for presents at Christmas and all the family love them, too."

So, we present, for your entertainment . . .

The Sunday Post 7th July 1946

The Sunday Post 28th July 1946

The Sunday Post 12th March 1950

The Sunday Post 25th June 1950

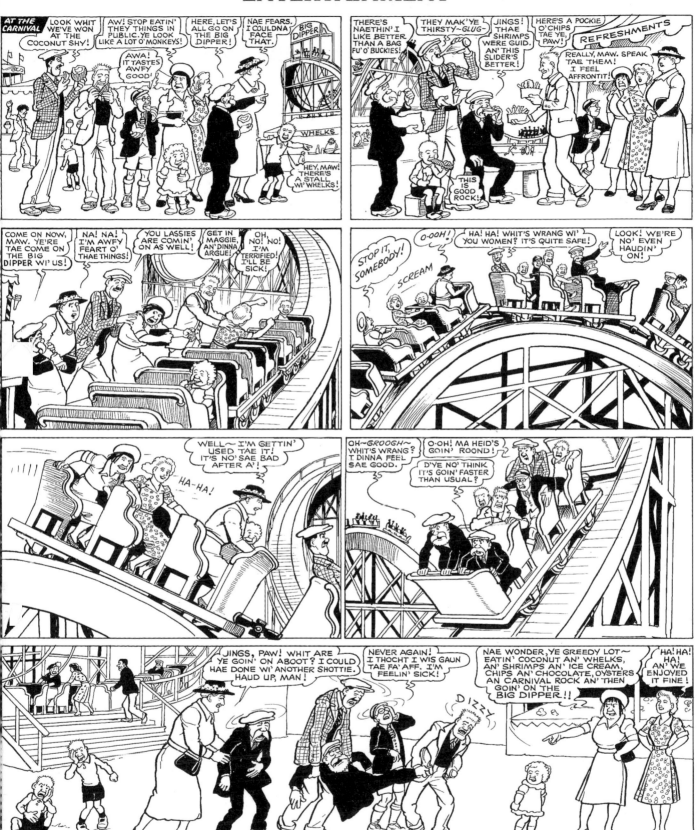

The Sunday Post 23rd July 1950

The Sunday Post 24th August 1952

ENTERTAINMENT

The Sunday Post 24th June 1951

The Sunday Post 9th August 1964

The Sunday Post 7th November 1965

A RICHT SHOWIN' UP

Another 'richt showin' up' for the Broons.

LORRAINE KELLY has become a well-known face as presenter of GMTV, as well as frequent other television appearances and in her own fitness video.

"The Broons and Oor Wullie made my Sunday," she says. "I thought they were posh because they had a 'but and ben' ". She says that of the Oor Wullie strips there are "Too many to choose" to name a favourite. The Bairn is a firm favourite character from The Broons and Lorraine is a proud mum to her own 'bairn', Rosie.

Lorraine's most vivid memory of The Broons involves "Daphne's new boyfriend being half French and half Polish" — turns out he was a 'FRENCH POLISHER' ". This is one of the many embarrassing moments where the family got a 'richt showin' up'. In the following pages we present a collection of calamities which will leave Wullie and the occupants of 10 Glebe Street 'black affronted' and should leave you with a smile on your face.

The Sunday Post 6th October 1946

A RICHT SHOWIN' UP

The Sunday Post 8th May 1949

The Sunday Post 8th December 1946

A RICHT SHOWIN' UP

The Sunday Post 4th December 1949

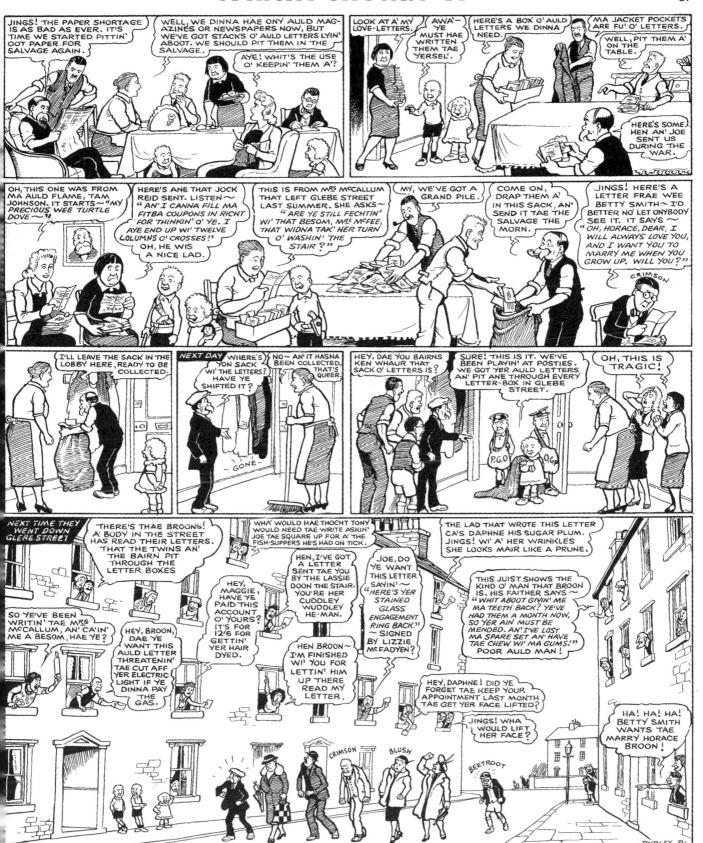

The Sunday Post 29th February 1948

A RICHT SHOWIN' UP

The Sunday Post 2nd April 1950

The Sunday Post 8th March 1953

A RICHT SHOWIN' UP

The Sunday Post 15th July 1951

The Sunday Post 22nd March 1953

A RICHT SHOWIN' UP

The Sunday Post 12th April 1953

A RICHT SHOWIN' UP

The Sunday Post 10th September 1967

BIG BAIRNS

THOSE BROONS men are a richt bunch o' big bairns, and no mistake. But, in this section, we'll be looking at the wee fowk who feature in the Fun Section.

BAIRNS

IT'S not just the grown-ups in Glebe Street who act like kids. There are the twins,

Horace and the Bairn, not forgetting Wullie and his pals. These bairns have been a source of some of the most memorable Fun Section moments. And, while the adults might behave like children sometimes, the bairns can outsmart them, more often than not.

It's child's play, as you're about to see.

The Sunday Post 12th May 1946

The Sunday Post 19th April 1953

The Sunday Post 8th September 1946

The Sunday Post 7th February 1954

The Sunday Post 9th October 1949

The Sunday Post 25th February 1968

88

BAIRRNS

The Sunday Post 16th February 1964

LAW AND ORDER

P.C. MURDOCH, wide of stomach and flat (rather then fleet) of foot is a favourite face from the Fun Section, having appeared frequently in The Broons strips alongside his more regular appearances as both friend and foe of Oor Wullie.

Murdoch and his comic strip colleagues on the force are a reminder of the days of the village bobby, on his bike and not in a squad car, the days before spray paint, when chalking on walls was an offence punishable by a strong ticking off. Burglars were always pretty easy to catch. Not surprising, given their tendency to wear hooped shirts and carry bags marked 'SWAG'. And the only hint of trouble within the force was when Murdoch was caught having a sneaky puff on his pipe.

A more innocent time? Perhaps. But it is an innocence that survives in the pages of the Fun Section, as well as the pages that follow.

These unique and rarely seen illustrations were originally part of an Oor Wullie story commissioned to promote road safety for cyclists.

LAW AND ORDER

The Sunday Post 15th December 1946

The Sunday Post 27th August 1967

LAW AND ORDER

The Sunday Post 1st October 1967

LAW AND ORDER

The Sunday Post 19th November 1967

The Sunday Post 30th May 1965

The Sunday Post 28th April 1968

LADS AND LASSIES

GLASGOW MSP and newspaper columnist, Dorothy-Grace Elder speaks fondly of The Broons and Oor Wullie and sums up their appeal to her as, "Nostalgia — I'm delighted that one publisher can produce innocent humour in a nasty age. The artwork is top class. It always was."

Asked to pick a favourite strip, she says, "I enjoy them all," adding, "I'm worried about Wullie though, since most buckets are plastic nowadays and he can't sit so easily on them."

And, she also adds, the characters appeal to more than just Scots. A vivid memory is, "The sight of my German friend, Effie, falling on the floor laughing at a Broons annual. Effie demands one every Christmas. She adores the Broons and has picked up all the nuances of their speech. She even adapts her own German name to sound more Broons-like."

The Broons have even crept into her political life. She says, "In the Scottish Parliament, I privately nickname some of the characters after The Broons — and Donald Dewar has to be Hen Broon for his tall, cadaverous frame and his ceaseless quest for the next snack!"

Swiftly leaving aside the world of politics, snacking is a hobby shared by her favourite character. "Daphne, because you feel sorry for her compared with vivacious Maggie. But Daphne is a warm hearted, sympathetic character." To this, she adds, "When I was a child, Daphne was a total frump," though notes that Miss Broon has blossomed somewhat in later years.

Daphne, Maggie, Maw and the Bairn . . . The Broon women are often a mystery to the menfolk, just as lassies leave Oor Wullie baffled. The following pages concentrate on how the lads and lassies get along in the Fun Section . . . or don't get along, which is often the case.

The Sunday Post 1st September 1946

LADS AND LASSIES

LADS AND LASSIES

The Sunday Post 9th March 1947

LADS AND LASSIES

The Sunday Post 27th April 1947

The Sunday Post 22nd June 1947

LADS AND LASSIES

The Sunday Post 17th March 1963

LADS AND LASSIES

The Sunday Post 19th May 1963

The Sunday Post 13th September 1953

LADS AND LASSIES

EDUCATION

Schooldays . . . the best days of your life? For Oor Wullie and the twins, the answer would be a resounding, "Nae fear!" In fact, the only one who seems to enjoy school is Horace, the brainbox of Glebe Street. He is often to be found at the dinner table, up to his elbows in books, happily working away at his homework. In this final section, we see Oor Wullie at school . . . or out of it, if he can get away with it . . . as well as a selection of strips in which Wullie and The Broons find that you don't have to be in a classroom to be taught a lesson.

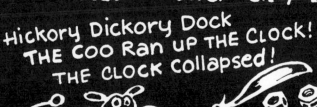

The Sunday Post 6th October 1946

The Sunday Post 12th December 1948

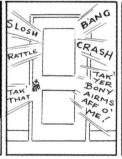

The Sunday Post 31st August 1947

The Sunday Post 9th September 1956

EDUCATION

The Sunday Post 23rd August 1959

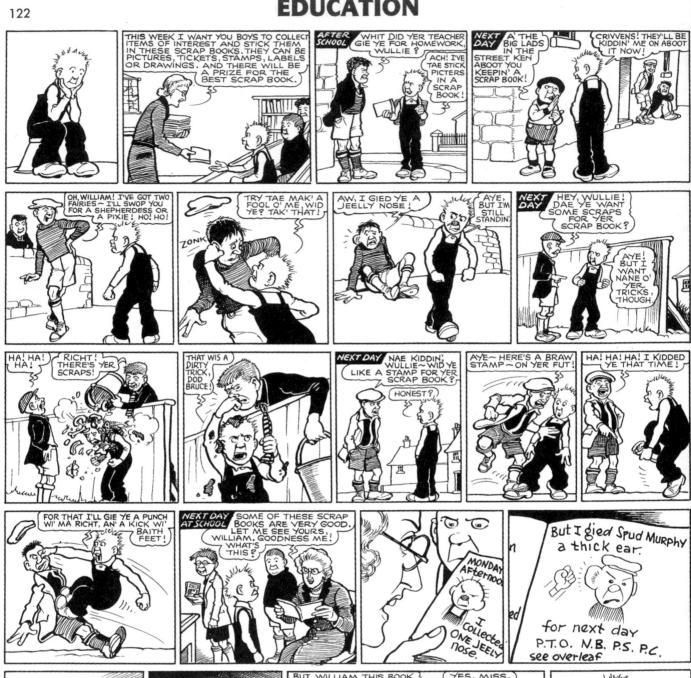

EDUCATION

The Sunday Post 13th October 1963

The Sunday Post 17th June 1951

AT HAME

FOR over sixty years, OOR WULLIE AND THE BROONS have been regarded by their readers as part of the family. And for these characters, home is definitely where the heart is.

Sir Tom Farmer CBE, chairman of Kwik-Fit has long been a fan of The Fun Section, saying, "The Broons and Oor Wullie are extended members of my family — Sunday morning, home from Mass and we all gathered round the fireplace in our kitchen. My Mum would be making lunch, Dad reading the sports section and seven children "fighting" over The Broons and Oor Wullie. The lucky winner would lie on the floor surrounded by brothers and sisters and would read out the escapades of the week gone by — what fun — The Broons and Oor Wullie were like Aunties, Uncles and cousins to us.

"Oor Wullie, Fat Bob and all the others, their antics were like ours, with our "pals" in the street, chalking on walls, fighting, our Mothers shouting for us to come in for tea and our Father scrubbing the backs of our necks.

"The Broons . . . that family was our family — they had a Granpaw, we had a Grandma. They had a Mum, Dad and lots of children — when they went to the But 'n' Ben, we wanted to go away too. Whether they were happy or sad, we were too.

"The Broons — Oor Wullie . . . They were definitely part of our family and today in the year 2000, I still open my Sunday Post at their pages to see what has happened to them all in the week gone by."

Some happy memories there, with more to follow, as we invite you to join The Broons and Oor Wullie "At Hame".

The Sunday Post 20th February 1949

The Sunday Post 24th February 1946

The Sunday Post 14th August 1949

The Sunday Post 17th March 1946

The Sunday Post 21st April 1963

AT HAME

The Sunday Post 29th March 1964

The Sunday Post 30th January 1949

AT HAME

The Sunday Post 9th August 1964

The Sunday Post 8th May 1949

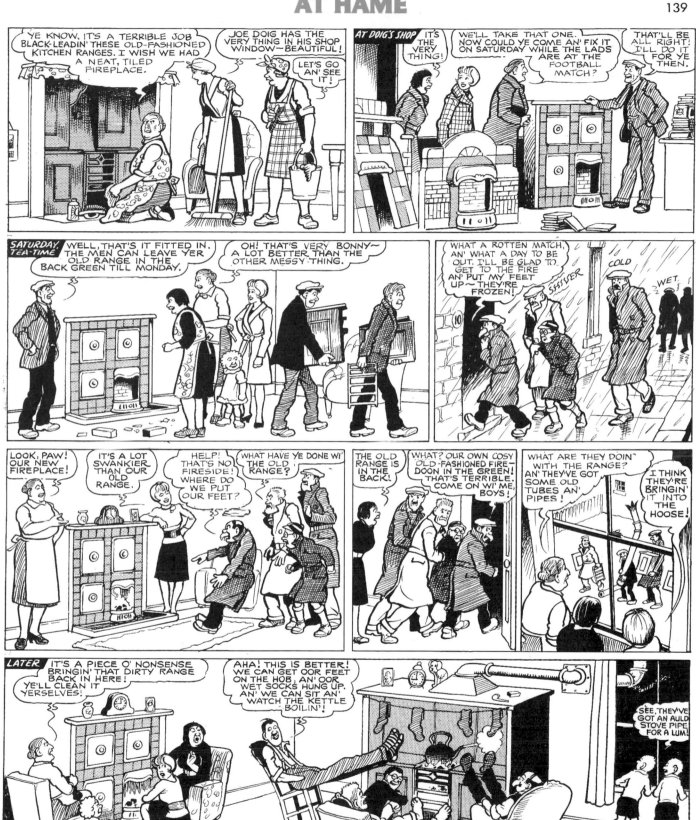

The Sunday Post 17th January 1954

FAMOUS LAST WORDS

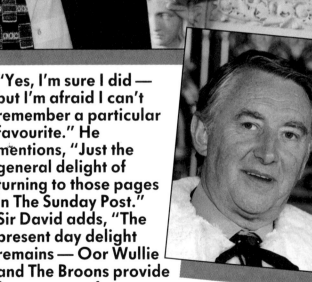

IF the title sounds ominous, don't panic. There are two further famous fans with some words to share. Appropriately enough, one of these fans shares the famous 'Broon' surname. Craig Brown, manager of the Scotland Football Team has also 'met' the Family. As he recalls, "Obviously my favourite is the one which featured my brother, Jock, and me." Jock Brown, Craig's brother, was, at the time a well known football commentator. "Jock has a framed copy of that particular strip . . .

"Oor Wullie, too, has been a favourite over the years," he says, while he admits to having a personal favourite among his namesakes. "Yes. Granpaw Broon. He reminded me of my own grandfather."

Another of Granpaw's admirers is Sir David Steel, now Baron Steel of Aikwood, of Ettrick Forest, in the Scottish Borders, a journalist and broadcaster, as well as being co-founder of the SDLP. When asked if he had a favourite strip, he says, "Yes, I'm sure I did — but I'm afraid I can't remember a particular favourite." He mentions, "Just the general delight of turning to those pages in The Sunday Post." Sir David adds, "The present day delight remains — Oor Wullie and The Broons provide for so many of us a direct and continuing link to our children." And that, as Granpaw Broon might put it, is "No' bad, at a'!"

Craig and Jock Brown made a guest appearance as 'cousins' in the strip published on November 7th, 1993. The artwork is by the then-current Fun Section artist, Ken Harrison.

OCH! THE BAIRN MEANT THE FANCY DRESS CHARITY MATCH OUR DAPHNE AND MAGGIE ARE PLAYIN' IN. HA! HA!

I LIKE THE LOOK O'THON LASSIE. MAYBE I'LL GIE HER A CALL UP.

CONTROVERSY HERE AS MAW BROON PUTS IN A TOUCHLINE TACKLE.

CHEEKY DREEP!

LEAVE MY LASS BE!

JINGS!

HAW! THEY'LL NO' GET THE BA' AROOND DAPHNE.

ON BEHALF OF OOR WULLIE AND THE BROONS, THE EDITOR WOULD LIKE TO
THANK KENNY DALGLISH AND SIR THOMAS RISK FOR THEIR KIND WISHES.
PARTICULAR THANKS FOR INTERVIEWS AND SHARED MEMORIES GO TO CRAIG
BROWN, DOROTHY-GRACE ELDER, SIR TOM FARMER CBE, SIR ALEX FERGUSON
CBE, GWYNETH GUTHRIE, LORRAINE KELLY, ALLY McCOIST, DOROTHY PAUL,
ROSAMUNDE PILCHER, SIR DAVID STEEL AND ROB WAINWRIGHT.
WITH SPECIAL THANKS TO THE LATE DUDLEY D. WATKINS, WHO ILLUSTRATED
ALL OF THE CLASSIC STRIPS COLLECTED HERE.

Printed and Published in Great Britain by D. C. Thomson & Co., Ltd., 185 Fleet Street, London EC4A 2HS.
© D. C. THOMSON & CO., LTD., 2000 **ISBN 0-85116-740-3**

OBAN

LO●
LOM●